JOURNEY *of* HOPE

An Everyday Guide for Adults with Dyslexia

Dr. Tracy Johnson

The resources in this book are provided for informational purposes only and should not be used to replace the specialized training and professional judgement of a healthcare or mental healthcare professional.

Neither the author nor the publisher can be held responsible for the use of the information provided within this book. Always consult a trained professional before making any decision regarding treatment for yourself or others.

Journey of Hope
Outline

Chapter 1   How To Diagnose Dyslexia 15

What is Dyslexia? 16

What Causes Dyslexia? 16

What Are Some Symptoms of Dyslexia? 16

How Do I Know if I Have Dyslexia? 17

Chapter 2   I Have Dyslexia; Where Can I Get Help? 19

Help with Reading and Writing Skills 19

Help for College Students. 20

Help for Job Seekers 24

Help in the Workplace 27

How Do I Disclose My Dyslexia? 31

Chapter 3   Social Life And Dyslexia. 35

At a Restaurant 36

At Parties or Gatherings 38

At Places of Worship 40

Chapter 4   Personal Challenges. 43

Driving 43

Personal Business. 45

Single Parents with Dyslexia 48

Voting. 51

Chapter 5   How To Support An Adult With Dyslexia. 53

Parental Relationships 54

Personal Relationships 56

The Role of Educators in the Community 58

Assistive Technology 60

Chapter 6   The Successful Person With Dyslexia:
What Makes Us Shine 63

Foreword

I was honored to be asked to write the foreword for *Journey of Hope: An Everyday Guide for Adults with Dyslexia*. I discovered the world of dyslexia almost twenty years ago through my son, Matthew, who is living with dyslexia. During that time, I was graced with this wonderful connection to Tracy Johnson. For all of those adults diagnosed, misdiagnosed, or never diagnosed with dyslexia, it has not been easy to navigate life through the complicated journey of an intelligent, yet unique mind, feeling stupid but yet able to accomplish so many things that others couldn't. The trauma of not being able to learn to read early remains a small hole in one's psyche for life. Even with success, those with dyslexia never feel quite good enough. As Tracy explains, their minds are structured differently which affects processing written language. Dyslexia is linked to genes; therefore, it's found in families.

Literacy is crucial to everyday life for safety, health, and livelihood. There are very successful people with dyslexia, but it's also true that when tested, over half of our prison population is living with dyslexia. Learning to read, the foundation of our educational system, shouldn't be a matter of luck. Dyslexia is on a spectrum, so it's easier for some to learn to read than it is for others, as Tracy shares through her journey. Learning to read and to succeed in school hasn't gotten much better since Tracy's days in her public schools. Over 60 percent of Philadelphia students are reading at a below-basic level. As Tracy explains in this book, the limits placed on an adult who can't read signs, menus, instructional manuals, medication bottles, or even a bedtime story make everyday life harder but also sadder. Yet those living with dyslexia, if given a chance, will work hard to succeed and become successful like Tracy and so many others. The work produced by people with dyslexia is found in our museums, libraries, movie theaters, and runways. The beauty of their abilities is on full display as we walk past their architectural and landscaping designs in every city throughout the world. These gifts have been misunderstood and under-appreciated for too long. Because of their dyslexia, they have the empathy and a shared vision of caring and understanding to help those around them.

I've known Tracy for many years. We've worked together, laughed, cried, and supported each other and our work on behalf of those less fortunate than Tracy and my son. Feeling fortunate isn't something that comes easily on most days and in most situations for those living with dyslexia, but Tracy also knows that in spite of those tough times and that hole in her psyche, she is blessed to be one of the lucky ones. Over the years, life had a way of bringing people into her life to encourage her, and her experiences provided the material that would become each chapter of this book. She overcame each hurdle. Her resilience led her forward to believe she could meet these challenges, and she stayed the course to become the successful woman she is today. She has come to define herself by her strengths and not her weaknesses.

Tracy partnered with me to begin our first Dyslexia Adult Support Group. I watched her during the group's discussions. She understood exactly what each person needed to hear. This book reflects her knowledge and insight into what adults living with dyslexia are facing every day. More importantly, Tracy has the instincts to know what they are feeling and how to speak truth to those emotions in a way that is both real and comforting. She knows where they are, where they are going, and what they will need to navigate each step along this path.

Journey of Hope: An Everyday Guide for Adults with Dyslexia continues Tracy's journey in her efforts to pay it forward for others. Most importantly, this book reflects what our society overlooks, and that is that real intelligence has a practical component. It has little to do with abstract education and everything to do with making sense of knowledge in a way that benefits people. Someone said adversity builds character, but someone else said adversity reveals character. I think this book will help you to both reveal and build your true character and guide you through a journey that isn't always easy. As Tracy has shown, it is possible, and you will be better and happier as a result of the journey.

Diane Reott
October 14, 2020

Introduction

This book was written to address the special needs of a special group of people who are living with dyslexia. Their needs also vary. The needs of an adult with dyslexia are quite different from those of a child with dyslexia who is still in school. While children are guided by their teachers to learn new skills and strategies, adults with dyslexia are exposed to the demands of parenthood and the workplace with practically no assistance.

The purpose of this book is to provide a resource tool for adults living with dyslexia, a specific learning disorder that mainly affects one's ability to read and write proficiently. It provides tips and suggestions to guide you through some of the obstacles you will encounter as you navigate life with dyslexia. There is also a section designed to be a guide for families who need to support their loved ones with dyslexia as well as members of the community who interact with them in educational, workplace and social environments. In addition, I have included encouraging quotes to help elevate your self-image and narratives of my own personal stories all in a bid to clarify your own understanding. As you embark on your journey of hope, this book will assist you in discovering the special person you truly are. You may feel frustrated or discouraged, but don't give up! All I ask is that you stay positive with hope, faith, and genuine love for yourself because help is on the way.

I was encouraged to write this book because of my own experience with dyslexia. From an early age at school, I painfully struggled with reading and writing. From the sixth grade through high school, I was placed in special education classes. This resulted in severe damage to my self-confidence and self-esteem, and my growing-up years were extremely difficult.

We are all guilty of negative thinking and self-berating in some form, and sometimes it can be difficult to turn off and silence the negative chatter in our minds. We are our own worst critics! If you suffer from dyslexia, you know all too well how the negative chatter can affect your mindset and your wellbeing. Many individuals with dyslexia struggle with low self-confidence, low self-esteem, and negative self-talk. *Self-talk* is defined as an internal dialogue or a conversation with the self. More often than not, people with dyslexia repeat unpleasant words, such as *stupid* and *retarded,* in reference to themselves. Their peers use other words to taunt them in school. While these unfortunate words do not describe their identities or abilities, most people with dyslexia gradually slip into the habit of identifying themselves with the names they have been called every time they misspell a word or make a mistake. Is it any wonder that adults with dyslexia often suffer from lack of self-confidence and poor self-esteem? I want to remind you that you are valuable and you have the power to view yourself in a more positive light.

My story started out just like anyone else's: a young girl who battled the inconvenient, and sometimes very painful, odds of a learning disorder. But I grew into adulthood to attain the heights of academic achievement. If I can do it, so can you.

There is passion within the pages of this book. That passion is to help others avoid the pitfalls that I encountered on my own journey. It is also to assist you to surmount the challenges of dyslexia far more easily than I did. I wish I'd had the privilege of access to this sort of information and guidance on my journey, but I derive great joy in the satisfaction that this book will make a remarkable difference in your own life. I wish each and every one of you nothing but the very best on your journey of awareness.

A Special Note

Dyslexia often creates many inconsistencies in an individual's life. Individuals with dyslexia may be gifted in some areas and have considerable deficits in other areas. Additionally, their cognitive skills may change over time. Dyslexia can have a traumatic and long-term effect on self-esteem.

Dr. Johnson poignantly reveals her academic struggles from childhood through adulthood. Although she was placed in special education classes in the sixth grade, she never felt she reaped any benefits from the special education system. Despite feelings of anxiety, depression, low self-esteem, inadequacy, and at times, suicidal thoughts, Dr. Johnson's courageous transparency is a testament of her steadfast faith, determination, and resilience amid adversity.

Journey of Hope: An Everyday Guide for Adults with Dyslexia serves as a catalyst to help adults with dyslexia and offers invaluable tips and resources to promote educational success and emotional-social well-being. This book offers a refreshing addition to the topic of dyslexia due to its specific focus on adults with dyslexia. Dr. Johnson provides real-life experiences and proposes a blueprint to effectively manage and overcome obstacles associated with dyslexia. Readers will gain insight regarding various manifestations of emotional, academic, employment, and social challenges that might be encountered.

Dr. Johnson's miraculous journey offers hope, encouragement, and will inspire adults with dyslexia and anyone who struggles with anxiety, depression, academic challenges, and a sense of self-worth. Dr. Johnson is a vessel of hope!

~Dr. Rahmanda Salamatu Campbell, Founder and Executive Director of The Reading Clinic, Inc., Dyslexia Services for Children and Adults Supervisor, Special Education Teacher Candidates, Department of Special Education, West Chester University of Pennsylvania

Special Dedication

I dedicate this effort to an amazing woman, Judith Mazer, who is also my co-author on this book project. Judith has two beautiful daughters, one of whom has dyslexia. At a time when there were insufficient services and resources to guide and educate people about dyslexia, Judith embarked on the Herculean effort to educate herself so that she could empower her daughter to be the best person she could possibly be. Judith became a certified reading specialist so that she would be equipped to empower her daughter, but also to help other children and adults dealing with dyslexia. I met Judith when I was first identified as having dyslexia, and she tutored me with the Wilson Reading System. At that time, she not only embraced me as a student, but also permitted our relationship to evolve into a mother-daughter one. Throughout my life journey, Judith has encouraged, supported, and loved me as her own. Remarkably, she was also my tutor for all three of my college degree programs. Words truly fail me in my attempt to express just how indebted and grateful I feel toward this wonderful woman who has been an integral part of my life. My sincere gratitude goes far beyond Judith's patience and dedication in helping me surmount my challenges with dyslexia. I am equally grateful for everything she did to transform me into the accomplished young woman I am today. To this great, wonderful, and noble woman I say, "Thank you, Mom Judy!"

Acknowledgements

I am deeply grateful to the following individuals who have generously contributed their time and insights, and without whom this book could not have been published: Steve Walker, Judith Mazer, Dr. Eileen McGovern, Dr. Rachmanda Campbell, Dr. Yimoi Grant, Claudia Koochek, Erica Marie, Cheryl Hackett, Jodi Button, Krista Nelson, Diane Reott, Paul Shump, Wendy Smith, Eileen Tait-Acker, Dr. Jacqueline Foster Ali, and Mary Murrill. In addition, I sincerely thank my wonderful family and friends for their ongoing support throughout this project.

Close Encounters
I Become Aware

We have all experienced a life event that has had an unforgettable and dramatic effect on us. Mine happened on the day I met my biological father for the first time when I was 20. Not having a father around was not that uncommon in my neighborhood. As a matter of fact, most of my friends rarely spoke of having a father in the house. Although we did not talk about it much, I still experienced a void and a longing created by the absence of a father.

Throughout my childhood, all of my questions about who my father was and what he looked like were usually met with vague and inconsistent responses. Growing up, I never stopped thinking about the mysterious man who was my father, but I gradually stopped asking my mother questions about him. In all fairness to her, my mother made a wonderful attempt at being both mother and father to my siblings and me, yet that did little to eliminate the feeling of emptiness that haunted my childhood.

Then one day everything changed. I was in my early twenties at the time, and I saw a television commercial about how to trace long-lost loved ones. The emotions regarding my father's absence surfaced again. The next day I called the organization, but they could not help me because the information at my disposal was rather scanty. I was discouraged. A few months passed, and I tried to forget about finding my father, but it was futile. I was obsessed. I was talking with my godmother on the phone one morning about my desire to find my father, and she volunteered some information about who he was. "I'm surprised you didn't know the truth," she said. I was shocked at what she'd told me—about his upbringing, where he lived when he was a teenager, etc. Armed with this knowledge, I decided to become my own private investigator.

I called a few people from my old neighborhood. I met one man who not only knew who my father was, but he was a close friend of his. I didn't know it at the time, but he had just been talking with my father on the phone. The very next day I received a phone call from my father. When I heard his voice for the first time, it felt like my heart dropped into the pit of my stomach. After talking for a while, we agreed to meet later that day somewhere in North Philadelphia.

With a feeling of trepidation, I arrived thirty minutes early. Butterflies danced in my stomach. I had an image in my head of what he looked like, that we would have the same eyes and smile as me. I kept checking my watch. Then I saw a very tall African-American man walking toward me. He held a long-stemmed rose in his right hand. "Are you Tracy?" he asked. I replied in the affirmative. He asked to see a picture of my mother. I handed him a picture I'd taken of my mother last summer. His eyes softened. On confirming that I was indeed his daughter, he gave me an enormous hug. At that instant, the void left by the absence of a father disappeared.

Since that meeting, I have gained a whole new family. I have a wonderful stepmother who loves me as she would her own daughter, three stepbrothers, and a host of nieces, nephews, aunts, uncles, and cousins, all of whom I have become very fond of. We spend holidays together, and they support my educational endeavors. My new-found relationship with my father has changed my life significantly because I have discovered the part of myself that was missing, and I now feel loved and accepted. My dad and I knew that we could not make up for the lost years, so we resolved to make the best of the years ahead of us.

As it later turned out, my father had not only been missing from my life physically, but he was also the "missing link" as to why I have dyslexia. You see, my father also had dyslexia. All of my life growing up, my older sister and brother never struggled with academic challenges like I did. My father told me that he had struggled with reading and spelling in school and how difficult it was for him growing up. After my father and I got to know each other better, he became one of my best friends. I now had someone to talk to about my dyslexia because he was the only one in my family who really understood how I felt. But what I loved most about my dad was his encouragement on those "dyslexic days" or a day when I simply didn't seem to be able to read or spell anything right when I was in college. I could always count on my dad to say, "Baby girl, you can do it," or, "I have dyslexia too, but that didn't stop me from being a sergeant in the army!" At other times he would say, "Don't ever let anyone tell you that you can't do anything because you have dyslexia." My father unfortunately passed away on April 28, 2010. While I truly miss my dad for so many things, I miss him the most on those really bad dyslexic days because I could always count on him for an encouraging word to keep me going. What made it all so special was that it came from one heart to another!

My Dad, Sergeant Alexander (Tony) Sheed

Chapter 1

How To Diagnose Dyslexia

"Challenges are what make life interesting, and overcoming them is what makes life meaningful."
- Joshua Marine

I struggled with dyslexia for most of my life, and it wasn't until I was diagnosed as an adult that I understood it and was able to get the help that I needed. When I was in grade school I was placed into a special education class because I couldn'tkeep up with my classmates. In spite of my teachers' best efforts, my academic skills did not increase. By the time I reached high school, the teacher told our class not to consider a college education. I really thought I could do better but did not know how to get help. This chapter provides insight into what dyslexia is, how to know if you have it, and where to get help. If you suspect you have dyslexia there are many resources listed in this chapter to help you get started. Remember, we are all human, and everyone has his or her own struggle. Having dyslexia is hard enough without any help or support, so know that you are not alone.

What is Dyslexia?

Dyslexia is a specific learning disorder that affects the part of the brain that is responsible for how a person learns to read, write, and spell. It has nothing to do with intelligence. In fact, most people who have dyslexia are of average or above-average intellect and can lead very successful lives.

What Causes Dyslexia?

Dyslexia is often a generational condition. This means it can be inherited from a parent, grandparent, aunt, or uncle. Yet, it can also skip a generation.

What Are Some Symptoms of Dyslexia?

The symptoms of dyslexia in adults are similar to those in children. There are numerous symptoms of dyslexia, but the more common ones appear below. You might find difficulty with a number of items listed here or just a few.

- Reading (silently and/or aloud)
- Understanding or remembering what has been read
- Spelling correctly
- Managing time effectively
- Learning a foreign language
- Memorizing facts or numbers
- Doing math problems
- Confusing left from right
- Organizing thoughts and task

How Do I Know if I Have Dyslexia?

If you think you might have dyslexia, the following resources might help you to find a testing location:

- Check with your doctor for a referral
- Call the psychology department of a local college or university
- Ask a reference librarian at your library
- Call the local Office of Vocational Rehabilitation (OVR)
- Explain your need to the local branch of the International Dyslexia Association (IDA). See the Resource Page at the end of this book for more information.

CHAPTER 2

I Have Dyslexia;
Where Can I Get Help?

"We are all different; don't judge,
understand instead."
- Roy T. Bennett

Although I struggled with reading and writing throughout my school years and was told by my high school teacher not to consider college, I thought I could do better. Years later, as an adult, I became aware of dyslexia, got tested, and was diagnosed. I found a tutor to increase my reading and writing skills and completed my college career. I found the help I needed through each step of this journey to reach my goal. This chapter is designed to help you get started no matter where you are in life.

Help with Reading and Writing Skills

- Local Centers for Literacy: https://centerforliteracy.org/

- Local branch of the International Dyslexia Association: https://dyslexiaida.org/

- The 411 on Disability
  http://lifeafterieps.com/
  whats-the-411-on-disability-disclosure/

- Local high school or school district offices for a list of reading tutors

- If possible, ask for a tutor who understands the learning challenges of someone with dyslexia.

Help for College Students

It wasn't until I was in college that I no longer could depend on my teachers for guidance. It was difficult to keep up with the required workload of assignments and preparation for exams. I was lucky to find teachers and a tutor who understood my special learning needs and offered ongoing support. If you are a college student struggling with dyslexia and need guidance, here are some suggestions for what to do:

- Go to the Disability Support Service Office at your institution of higher learning to discuss your academic concerns.

- Bring copies of your high school IEP (Individualized Education Program), documentation of your disability, list of supports you have received during your education, and any recent test evaluations, as these are all required in order for you to receive academic support.

When you meet with your advisor/counselor, these are some questions you might wish to ask. They are referred to as *accommodations*.

- Are there tutors trained to help students with dyslexia?

- Is there a charge for tutoring?

- Can I bring a tape recorder to my classes?

- Are there note-takers available if I need one?

- Can I have extra time for assignments and tests?

- How large are the class sizes?

- Is there any assistive technology that I can use?

- Is there someone who can read the test questions to me during exams or quizzes?

- Are there quiet places to study on campus?

A Village

"It takes a village to raise a child," so goes the popular saying. It also takes a village to help and support every successful adult with dyslexia. I encourage you to seek out and identify such individuals who currently live in your community. Your "village" can include family members or friends who are always there to correct your spelling or edit your emails, a coworker or supervisor who understands what you meant to write even though the wording may not be quite right, and members of your local place of worship who can give you hope and strength during the difficult times. One person who is definitely a part of my village is a close member of my family. When I received my bachelor's degree in psychology from Cabrini University, I wanted to send a group invitation by email to friends and family for a graduation party. As I prepared to send the email, I realized it needed be reviewed for spelling errors. On reading the invitation, my family member called immediately to tell me that she had caught an embarrassing mistake that would have offended my guests. This reminded me that no matter how capable we think we are; we will always need that person in our "village" to help identify embarrassing errors in our work.

Try this!
College Students

If this is the first time you are asking for accommodations, role play with a friend the important questions you would like to ask.

Help for Job Seekers

- Make a list of your skills and strengths, what you are good at, and what you can bring to a workplace. Then, ask a friend or family member to help you find a job to meet those skills.

- Before you apply for a job, find out about the company's disability policies.

- Learn what your job duties might be and decide if you feel capable of handling them.

Prepare for an Interview

- Think ahead about your strengths so you can discuss them during an interview. Be prepared to discuss at least one weakness and how you are working to overcome it.

- Have a paper copy of an application filled in as a guide in case you need to complete computer applications on the spot.

- Create a list of keywords you may have to use in filling out important documents.

When filling out a job application, make a list of everything you can think of that you will need to enter into the computer. This might include:

- Name and address of the high school you attended

- Name and address of a college or trade school that you attended

- Name of companies, addresses, and dates where you were previously employed

- Name of former boss(es) or supervisor(s) and their contact information

- Name of people and contact information you would like to list as references

- List your skills (i.e.., computer software programs, cashier, oral communication skills, problem solving, etc.)

Try this!
Job Seeker

Ask someone you know well to help you create a list of your strengths for an interview.

Help in the Workplace

The workplace can be the most challenging obstacle people with dyslexia can face. Those struggling with dyslexia or other learning disorders often experience unemployment and underemployment. They may even find themselves having to work at a job that is just not a good match for their strengths and weaknesses. At other times, they are unable to do what they are actually passionate about. The end result is that they are unable to earn sufficient income to meet their needs. These situations can lead to a downward spiral that can negatively affect other areas of their lives. I work as an enrollment counselor for a university. My job schedule requires that I write numerous emails. This takes me longer than most people because of my poor spelling skills. I need to spend time checking what I have written, yet I still commit errors. Sometimes I am called into the office because of these mistakes. Some of my coworkers demonstrate understanding when I explain to them that I have dyslexia, but others can be cruel. Because of my dyslexia, I believe I have been passed over for promotions and pay increases.

Please note the following vital points at the workplace:

- You should not be discriminated against. Dyslexia is now covered under the Americans With Disabilities Act (ADA).

- If you have a previous evaluation for dyslexia, you might want to update it to make sure that your current skills are accurate.

- To disclose or not to disclose: You are not required to disclose that you have dyslexia or any other disability for that matter; the choice of disclosure is simply yours to make.

Advantages of disclosure: You may receive the support and accommodations you need to succeed on the job. Disclosure also means you are taking courageous ownership of your challenges, and the fact that you are honest and forthcoming about your disability can often impress an employer. They cannot refuse to hire you as long as you can perform the essential functions of the job. Also, note that some employers choose to hire individuals with disabilities because there are tax incentives.

If you do not disclose: You may find yourself painfully struggling to keep up with the workload, especially since, in ignorance of your disability, your employer may not offer any accommodations to support you to be successful. Although you might "feel" like they will not hire you if you disclose at the end of an interview, this is not the case in most employment settings. If you do not disclose and the employer later discovers your disability because it is affecting your job performance, it may have a negative impact on your employment.

Only disclose your disability if you feel comfortable doing so or if it becomes an obvious issue. Be prepared for this eventuality, as you might have to present your Employment Evaluation to the Human Resources Department.

- Emphasize your strengths and your skill sets and what you are able to contribute to the organization.

- After spending some time at your new workplace, find a co-worker who understands your dyslexia to assist you if the need arises.

- If you need to send an email, first send it to yourself or to a friend to review it for mistakes.

- Make a list of words that you use most often in your current job to help avoid making spelling errors. Here are some examples for office work:
  - Calendar
  - Schedule
  - Supplies
  - Materials
  - Words used most often in your emails

Try this!
The Workplace

Now that you know your co-workers, select someone you think can help you with your workplace challenges. Discuss your needs and ask if they would be willing to assist you.

How Do I Disclose My Dyslexia?

Sometimes it can be difficult to talk about ourselves when it comes to personal matters, and this can be especially hard for people with dyslexia. When I was a young girl, my classmates teased me for being "stupid" because I couldn't spell the words on the blackboard. Nobody wanted to pick me for group projects because I was the "slow kid." While I did eventually receive tutoring and help for my dyslexia, those memories have stayed with me. So, when I approached adulthood—in college and in the workplace—I was always a bit guarded. I worried about being judged or penalized in some way for my dyslexia. While I can only speak for myself, I found that disclosing my dyslexia was a positive experience because it helped others to better understand me. Telling people about your dyslexia is a personal choice. If you decide to share this information, here are some suggestions of things you might say:

In the interview

"I want to share with you that I have a challenge with reading and writing, and it is called dyslexia." (Be prepared to explain how it directly affects you).

"I feel it is important for you to know that I have dyslexia. In order for me to be successful, I know that I will need . . ." (Explain what dyslexia is, if applicable). List the support you have had in the past and how they helped you to be successful. Always stay positive in your description and emphasize your strengths.

"Although I have dyslexia, I think I am a good fit for this position (discuss ways in which you believe you can benefit the workplace). I will sometimes need software programs that can read text aloud for me and to check my grammar and spelling, but many of these software programs are free and will be of no cost to you."

In social situations

"People with dyslexia are just like everyone else. It has nothing to do with how smart we are. We just learn things in a different way. Reading and writing might take us a bit longer, but we can use the newest tools of technology to help. Everyone has some challenges, but people with dyslexia are often very creative and successful in business and the arts like Bruce Springsteen. Even Albert Einstein had dyslexia!"

- If you don't feel comfortable talking about your dyslexia, you can get creative! Create a business card with your picture on the front and your challenges and strengths listed on the back.

Example:

I am Dyslexic.

My Strengths Are:
• Connecting with people
• Solving problems outside the box
• Thinking optimistically

Support & Resourses:
• Learning Ally
• Franklin Speaking Speller
• Spell Check
• Supportive Network
  of Family and Friends

Tracy Johnson
vesselsofhopevessels@gmail.com

CHAPTER 3

Social Life And Dyslexia

"If there is no struggle, there is no progress."
- Frederick Douglas

Your social life is an area where your dyslexia can present real challenges. People with dyslexia may shy away or refrain from attending social gatherings. For example, ordering dinner at a restaurant or going to classes may cause anxiety because of weak reading skills. Playing board games like a simple game of Scrabble might also be difficult for the person with dyslexia because it requires good spelling skills. The following are some suggestions to help you avoid embarrassment in social situations:

At a Restaurant

Eating out is one of the most popular social activities, but reading the menu can be a challenge for someone who has dyslexia. I will never forget how painfully embarrassed I was on a date with a gentleman friend. It was a warm, sunny day and we had gone to a water ice stand. After we read the menu, he asked what I wanted and I replied, "pine cola" instead of "piña colada." I felt so ashamed.

- Ask the server to recommend a popular choice if you are having trouble reading the menu.

- Look at pictures on the menu (if shown) and ask about them.

- Check the menu online if you know where you are going and make a choice ahead of time.

- Ask friends what they might choose. For example, you could say, "What are you going to order?"

- If it is appropriate, look around the room to see what other people are having, and ask for something that may look appealing to you.

- Ask your server what the specials are for the day, this may also be a way to try new foods that you my like.

- Ask which restaurant you are going to and check the menu on line ahead of time.

At Parties or Gatherings

Games are fun in a social gathering, but when you have dyslexia, it can put you in an uncomfortable position. One time, I was at my house playing a game with my cousins. The game required us to pick a partner, read the word on a card, then act it out. I couldn't read the word quickly enough and we lost the game. My cousin was very upset with me.

The following tips might help you feel more comfortable if you feel challenged:

- If there are games using words, partner with someone to help you who knows about dyslexia.

- When asked to read something aloud, politely ask if someone can read that part.

- Try to suggest a different game that doesn't use words.

Try this!
Social Situations

Make a list of restaurants and social activities you are most familiar with. You can make the suggestion of where to go or what to do.

At Places of Worship

Social activities can also take place in religious settings in the form of classes, discussion groups or recreational programs. During one early morning adult Sunday School session at my church, I was handed a book and asked to read a portion of the session aloud. Since it was my first day of class, I had not had a chance to read the material ahead of time. When I was called to read, I faked a coughing spell and excused myself to get a drink. I did this because I could not read the words. These suggestions can help you avoid shame while at the same time help you to realize your potential:

- Feel comfortable in confiding in the leaders of your activities about your dyslexia so they can better understand your challenges.

- If you are called upon to read aloud in classes or programs, ask if you may listen for that day.

- If you want to participate by reading, ask for a copy of any written material before to help you prepare. For example, there are, if you are Jewish, often group seders for the holiday of Passover. Arrange to find your part in the Passover Hagaddah before the Seder begins. This way you will be prepared to read.

Try this!
Place of Worship

Remember why you are there. Instead of focusing on your dyslexia, think of the ways in which this environment brings you joy and peace.

CHAPTER 4

Personal Challenges

"It doesn't matter how slow you go
as long as you don't stop."
– Confucius

Driving

Most people will not have any difficulty driving, but those with dyslexia can find the experience challenging when reading street signs, following directions, and trying to differentiate left from right. One day I was driving in New Jersey and the GPS system in my car told me to turn right. Because I confused my left and right, I turned the wrong way and drove an hour and a half in the wrong direction. Now, I think about what hand I write with, which is my right hand, and that is how I remember to turn right.

Here are a few helpful tips for when you are driving:

- To remember left from right, choose different colors to represent the directions of left and right. Tie matching color strings—one for left and one for right—to opposite sides of the steering wheel to help you remember.

- If possible, have a GPS system on your phone or in the car to listen to directions.

- Ask for landmarks if you are given verbal directions.

- Ask someone to write down the name of the streets you are looking for to compare with the street signs.

Personal Business

Handling personal business such as filling out forms and applications can be another challenging area for a person struggling with dyslexia. I had an appointment to visit a new doctor. My first challenge was reading the medical history form. The second challenge was to be able to spell the information that was needed to complete the form. I left many answers blank because I could not spell the words. When I saw the nurse, I gave her the excuse that I ran out of time. Now, I ask the doctor's office to send me the medical history form in the mail or on line to fill out at home.

The following is a list of suggestions to make this task easier for you:

- For banking, medical, insurance, or other personal forms, take someone with you, fill the forms out at home, or ask someone who works at the place of business to help you.

- When making big purchases, like buying a car or a house, take someone knowledgeable with you.

- Use a smartphone to look up the words you don't understand. This method gives you privacy.

When making a doctor's appointment, ask the office to send the medical history form to fill out at home.

If the office cannot provide this, the following is a list of some medical history information you can take with you to your appointment:

- Doctors' names and addresses
- Medications you are taking
- Allergies
- Injuries or surgeries
- List of family history of illnesses
- Hospitals where you have been treated

Remember: You do not have to sign anything when you are uncomfortable or unclear about its meaning or interpretation. If you feel pressured or rushed to sign any legal documents, you should take them home to review them with someone you trust.

Try this!
Personal Business

Look at your calendar for the week and prepare for any upcoming appointments.

Single Parents with Dyslexia

Dyslexia can be inherited from a parent, so if you have a child with dyslexia, there is a possibility you might have it too. Helping that child with language arts can be a challenging task when you have experienced similar struggles yourself. Add the lack of support at home, and your responsibilities can be overwhelming. The following suggestions might be useful in providing some help for you to help your child.

- Remember that having dyslexia does not mean lack of intelligence; offer your help in math or other areas of expression such as art or drama projects.

- Find a tutor to help your child with reading or writing homework tasks. The school should have a list of tutors training in dyslexia.

- If the school has not enrolled your child in a program to improve language related skills, the office can usually provide a list of private tutors for that purpose.

- Children with dyslexia often have enhanced skills in non-academic areas such as the arts or sports. It is important to provide the opportunity for them to participate in extra-curricular activities where they can excel.

- If you think you need to increase your own skills as well as those of your child, refer to Chapter 2 of this book to find tutoring help. Always insist on a tutor with knowledge of dyslexia.

Try This!
Helping Your Child

Make an appointment with your child's teacher or the school counselor to express your concerns and to find a capable tutor.

Voting

We are privileged to live in a democracy, and one of the most important things we can do as citizens is to vote. However, this process is not always an easy one for someone with dyslexia. On a recent election day, I entered the voting booth and was surprised to find there were several questions that required a *yes* or *no* answer. I was able to vote for the candidates, but it took too long for me to read the questions and understand the meaning; I had to leave them blank. In order to avoid this situation, you may find the following tips useful:

- Contact your local politicians' offices or political community group for information about the candidates and possible questions.

- Once you have educated yourself, obtain a sample ballot so you will know what to look for in the voting booth; you may take the ballot in with you.

CHAPTER 5

How To Support An Adult With Dyslexia

"Our greatest weakness lies in giving up.
The most certain way to succeed is always
to try just one more time."
– Thomas A. Edison

An adult with dyslexia can have serious challenges when it comes to home and personal life. Having dyslexia can interfere and complicate relationships with family, friends and community members who do not understand how to help. This chapter will provide suggestions for these people to better understand the needs of those with dyslexia and how to support them.

Parental Relationships

Being a parent is not easy, but having a child who has dyslexia can be difficult for both parents as they work together to support the child. In the family dynamic, one spouse also might be struggling with dyslexia. That difference can challenge couples when helping a son or daughter navigate through everyday tasks. The parent without dyslexia may often be the one to take on all of the burden in dealing with the daily activities of the child. If one parent has to carry the responsibility of helping the child or children with homework, finding ways to help the other partner feel useful or included will strengthen the family bonds.

- Help your spouse with dyslexia feel comfortable and valuable in sharing opinions about supporting your child. Be a good listener and discuss all ideas together.

- One way to include your spouse is to ask if he/she would like to be present as you are helping your child with homework.

- Arrange for your spouse to play a game with one child while another sibling is receiving help. You want to ensure everyone gets enough attention.

- Before a parent teacher meeting, talk to your spouse about what will be discussed, what contribution they might want to make, or questions to ask.

Personal Relationships

As the partner of an adult with dyslexia, your personal relationship can easily lead to feelings of frustration. It is important to understand why your partner struggles with everyday tasks like organization, verbal, and/or written communication, and directions. The following are some resources for you that might be helpful in developing a greater understanding of these challenges. In addition, those with dyslexia might suffer from feelings of inadequacy. Here you will find some suggestions of activities for quality togetherness time that can also promote greater self-esteem for you partner.

On line resources

- The HBO documentary, *Journey into Dyslexia.*

- Online articles

- *17 Things to Expect When you Love Someone Who Has Dyslexia* by Melanie Berliet

- *20 Things to Remember If You Love a Person with Dyslexia* by Cate Skolnik.

Togetherness activities

- Set aside a day and time each week for playing a game (cards, a board game), a shared activity (jig saw puzzle), or making plans for a celebration or event. If there are children, they can be included.

- Make a To Do list of household activities (repairs, cleaning, painting), plan a day to accomplish them, and cross them off as they are completed.

- Create a secret word or hand signal for your partner to use to indicate they are uncomfortable in a social situation

- Encourage your partner to talk to you when he/she feels frustrated and listen without judgment.

NOTE: Give your partner the opportunity to suggest an activity. Keep in mind, if it involves a game (or anything competitive) it should be something in which he/she can excel. We are *all* more motivated to participate when we think we can be successful!

The Role of Educators in the Community

The learning environment plays an important role in how students with dyslexia can cope. Thankfully, many educators do volunteer their time in places such as religious settings, literacy centers, libraries, and tutoring labs on college campuses, but they are not always trained to recognize a learning disorder. This chapter is to help those educators become aware of ways to encourage their students to feel as competent and confident as possible.

- When working with people you suspect have dyslexia, try to find multiple ways to teach them effectively. You can use videos, charts, pictures and other visual or auditory aids.

- Be as patient as you possibly can. It may take a person with dyslexia much longer to grasp or process the information you are sharing.

- Ask the students to repeat what was taught or discussed to ensure that they understand the information.

- Watch for signs of diversion or avoidance. You might see a student trying to avoid a task by covering the paper or talking to create a diversion.

- Be careful with the words you use when correcting a student. Use positive and encouraging words. For example, "That was a good try. Let's look at that again."

- When reviewing a student's written work, focus on the positive first. If the grammar or punctuation is incorrect but there is good content and a clear thought process, focus on these first.

Note: If you suspect that a student has dyslexia, refer to Chapter 1 of this book regarding symptoms of dyslexia, and/or refer them to the resources at the end of this book for expert help and guidance.

Assistive Technology

Technology has created great opportunities for people with dyslexia to function effectively in school, at work, and in everyday life. There are a growing number of choices that are functionally rich and cost effective to help you with your dyslexia.

Books (including textbooks)

Audiobooks are a great resource. Often these are recorded by actors or sometimes by the authors themselves (no computer voices).

Learning Ally (live voice recordings)
$135 for the year
https://learningally.org/

Audible (live voice recordings)
$14.95–Free content – *New York Times* and Get Book a Month
https://www.audible.com/

Website Articles

There are countless articles found on . . . It depends on what platform you are on and how you like to consume content.

Instapaper (website articles text to speech)
Free
https://www.instapaper.com/u

Siri or Google Assistant (text to speech)

Printed Text

Recently, this required expensive specialized scanner technology, but there are now free alternatives using smartphone cameras. This technology combination will make this accessible to a much larger audience.

Speechify (pictures to speech able context)
Free
https://www.getspeechify.com/

PDFs
NaturalRead (PDF text to speech)
Free
https://www.naturalreaders.com/

Speech to Text

Almost all writing software (messaging, email, word processor, etc.) has an embedded speech-to-text function. Combine these tools with help from a proofreader and you can deal with almost all of your writing needs.

CHAPTER 6

The Successful Person With Dyslexia: What Makes Us Shine

"A problem is a chance to do your best."
– Duke Ellington

The successful person with dyslexia could be a professional who is employed as a Chief Executive Officer (CEO). Such a person might also hold many other important positions such as a banker, teacher, pastor, or an entrepreneur. Many successful people living with dyslexia have to struggle. Spelling and reading still pose a very real challenge or barrier. They may have many accomplishments and competencies, yet are challenged in other areas such as academic settings or the workplace. The following are stories some of these people have shared about their achievements and tools they have used to help them become the successful people they are.

SUSAN MAZER

Having dyslexia is a part of who I am, but I have tried to never let it hold me back or define me. I have a master's degree in music, which I completed with honors. Currently, I am an arts administrator, performer, and on the faculty at Sacred Heart University. I wrote twelve instructional music books for Alfred Publishing, including one that sold over a quarter of a million copies. Over the years, I realized that I had to rely on my ears as much as my eyes. I found that if I read out loud what I had written, I would uncover more mistakes. Now, I use text-to-speech (TTS) software programs that will read what is on the page back to me. NaturalReader is a program that I recommend. Sometimes, I look and listen several times to be sure that everything is correct. It can be embarrassing to ask others to proofread your work, so let TTS software be your private editor. I could go on and list dozens of tools and tricks that I use to make living with dyslexia easier. However, the most important tip is to be kind to yourself. You can be intelligent and successful, and a spelling mistake or mispronounced word does not change that. Some tasks may take you longer to complete, but if they are always finished and done to the best of your ability, you should feel proud. Along the way, people will appreciate you for the special skills you hold that a typical learner may not possess. Do not believe that little voice that says, "You are not good enough." You *are* enough!

ELIZABETH TAKI

Elizabeth Takyi, who resides in England, is the founder and director of Aspire2inspireDyslexia CIC, an organization in the Wandsworth region of England that identifies and supports individuals with dyslexia and other specific learning disorders. She saw a gap in services offered for individuals with dyslexia in that area that could provide screening and assessment, confidence building, and employability training.

Growing up in the eighties, Elizabeth struggled in school to read and write until the age of fifteen and was bullied by her classmates. She became disruptive in class and got in trouble with teachers.

As a result, Elizabeth ended up in the bottom level of her class and dropped out of school at the age of sixteen without a diploma. When her friends enrolled in college, she felt pressured to attend with them but dropped out because of her learning difficulties. Suffering from a lack of self-confidence, Elizabeth also failed in the workplace. She hopped from one job to another when she felt she could not perform the tasks required of her and was ashamed to tell her employer of her difficulties.

The turning point in Elizabeth's life occurred when she was brave enough to enroll at South Bank University in London. Although she had doubts that she would succeed, she was motivated to better herself by having two young children at home. With the help of the study skills team and one-on-one tutoring, Elizabeth finally graduated with a certification to teach. It was more important to her, however, to help other individuals with dyslexia who were struggling within the educational system or the workplace. This led to the start-up in 2016 of Aspire2inspire and where she remains today.

PAUL SHUMP

Paul Shump blogs about making the most of dyslexia and the role of technology for people with dyslexia at www.dyscuss.org. He speaks from his own personal experience as a person with dyslexia who has navigated through the education system to achieve a BA in psychology from King's College. He has worked as a coach at the high school and college level, and at managing customer service. When he is not playing with new technology, Paul is on the golf course or building something with his young daughter. As an iPhone and iPad user, his most frequently used technology is the Apple digital assistant, Siri. He uses Siri to read emails and text messages and dictate responses. He uses Audible on a daily basis to read the news and books, and he relies on other technology tools for information sources for organizing and ideation.

DANYELE DOVE

I am passionate about helping people live their best lives and accomplish their goals. Through my work I am committed to empowering people to develop a life plan that will lead to self- discovery and ultimately career independence. My approach to helping is non-judgmental, and I cooperatively assist people to clarify their steps to reach their goals. I also draw from a variety of methods to create a tailored approach for each individual and situation. I have a Master of Social Work degree, and as a social worker I am direct, compassionate, and encouraging, combining my experience, education, and creativity with a down-to-earth approach to helping others.

As a person with dyslexia, I have always had to work harder. My friends could study and get what was needed for the test in thirty minutes, and it took me an hour and thirty minutes to retain the information. Dyslexia has taught me patience and acceptance. In school we are trained to think of our work quantitatively by our grades. As an adult, it's the quality of my work that determines my grades in life. I chose to be a social worker to help people know that they can improve their station in life with hard work and focus despite any challenges life has thrown at them. Dyslexia helped me recognize that life is not a competition; it has helped me appreciate the diversity and the complexities of learning. We all don't learn the same way, but we all can learn if given the opportunity.

STEVE WALKER

I am a self-taught engineer, inventor, and entrepreneur. I founded, grew, and sold more than five companies in my thirty-three-year career and have advised dozens of other organizations as a member of the Board of Directors, consultant, or volunteer. As the founder of IMBY Energy, I have put my engineering and business skills to work creating energy technology that will change the way people heat, cool, and power their homes all over the world. Like many entrepreneurs, I have achieved my success without higher education.

To be clear, I can read and write; it's just very slow and tends to be inaccurate. I can't spell anything. In fact, it's so bad that spell-checks still don't know what I am trying to say. Often, I need to Google something in a phrase to get the correct spelling for it.

Ordering food without reading the menu is a challenge. I ask people around me what they're having, ask the wait staff what is good, or if I see a passing meal that looks good, I will ask what it is.

When filling out government forms such as a license, I pick up or download the forms and have everything filled out beforehand.

If I need to fill in forms in writing—at a doctor's office, for example—I will often ask for help. I usually come up with an excuse and say that I have recently broken a hand or finger and it really hurts to write. Or I might say the writing will be so bad it won't be readable.

I let everybody know I have a hard time reading and writing, so most people who know me, work with me, or are my friends will accommodate . . . I just have to remind them. Sometimes, it's easy for people to forget how difficult it is for me to read and write. It took me a while to learn that they aren't ignoring me, they just simply forget.

When I Google things, I click on images and do most of my searches that way. That can be a big advantage, often being much faster than people who read through websites.

I always make an effort to not get myself into situations where I need to read or write. Very often I will ask if I can fill something out or read it later and then have someone help me.

I have not filled out checks or handled my bills for most of my life because any time I tried it was a bit of a disaster. So, either I hire someone to help, or my wife will handle all my personal bills and banking.

If I need to organize something that does not allow me the ability to get help to read or write, I try to use images and numbers as much as possible. I often number files and then I write the name of it afterwards, so if somebody else needs to know where it is, they can find it. I can remember numbers much more easily.

Fortunately, in the last ten years, new technology has made reading and writing much easier. I use Apple products, which are pretty good at reading and writing for me. Everything in this article I am dictating through an iPad. I download apps and try different ways to find the best technology of the day to help me read and write. Technology still has a long way to go, and most anything I have used has its flaws. It can be frustrating when the device I am using occasionally crashes. Hopefully, people will just keep working at it, and this will become easier as time goes on.

In general, the biggest tool is just letting people know that I have a hard time reading and writing, and it's kind of amazing how much people will help.

ABOUT THE AUTHOR

"Never, never, never give up."
– Winston Churchill

The story of Dr. Tracy Johnson is poignant and inspirational. Yet, she tells it with such candor, humility, grace, and passion. She recalls that, "One college counselor told me that I should give up." She did not give up. She was discouraged, but she was certainly not defeated. She worked for years as a custodian, cleaning school buildings for the Philadelphia School District. She knew she had more to offer and that she could be more. It seemed that everyone around her focused on her limitations and not on her potential.

Raised in Philadelphia, Pennsylvania, by a single mother, for years Tracy could not understand why she had difficulty learning basic math and English. She struggled even in special education classes. She was labeled "slow" by teachers and peers. A high school special education teacher once told her entire class that none of them had the ability for a college education. Her dyslexia, a learning disorder affecting the ability to learn to read and write, was not diagnosed until she became an adult. Later, she found a tutor to help strengthen her reading and writing skills using the Wilson Reading Program that employed multisensory instruction. Because of her strong faith, mentors, family, and friends, she was eventually accepted at Harcum College where she obtained an associate's degree with a 4.0 GPA.

Later, she received a bachelor of science from Cabrini College, graduating with high honors.

Tracy has turned her challenges into victories. She overcame poverty despite little support. Today, she is an accomplished lecturer and an advocate for people with learning disabilities, particularly dyslexia. She received an MA in multicultural education from Eastern University and an Honorary Doctorate of Science in Ministry from the Accredited School of Christian Ministry, Inc. Affiliated with Lancaster Bible College.

Tracy is founder and president of Vessels of Hope, a mentoring and networking organization for minority people with learning disabilities. She is a much sought-after speaker whose personal journey to academic achievement has inspired individuals with dyslexia and other learning disabilities, their parents and educators, as well as legislators and civic and business leaders. She is featured in the highly touted HBO documentary film, *Journey into Dyslexia: Great Minds Think Differently,* released in 2011. For further inquiries, feel at liberty to visit her website at Vessels of Hope, http://vesselsofhopevessels.org/. You can also email her at vesselsofhopevessels@gmail.com

Resources

Decoding Dyslexia (National Organization for Parents)
   http://www.decodingdyslexia.net/

DYCUSS, Engage Dyslexia (Paul Shump)
   www.dyscuss.org.

The International Dyslexia Association (IDA)
   https://dyslexiaida.org/

The Reading Clinic, INC
   https://readingclinicinc.org/

The 411- on –Disclosure
   http://lifeafterieps.com/whats-the-411-on-disability-disclosure

Vessels of Hope
   http://vesselsofhopevessels.org/

References

Apple. "IPad User Guide." Accessed September 22, 2020. https://support.apple.com/guide/ipad/spoken-content-ipad9a247097/ipados.

Berliet, Melanie. "17 Things to Expect When You Love Someone Who's Dyslexic." March 31, 2015. Accessed September 22, 2020. https://thoughtcatalog.com/melanie-berliet/2015/03/17-things-to-expect-when-you-love-someone-whos-dyslexic/.

The Mayo Clinichttp://www.mayoclinic.org/diseases-conditions/dyslexia/basics/symptoms/con-20021904.

Scolnik, Cate. "20 Things to Remember If You Love a Person With Dyslexia." Accessed September 22, 2020. https://www.lifehack.org/articles/lifestyle/20-things-remember-you-love-person-with-dyslexia.html.